MADE TO CHANGE THE WORLD

Small Group Study

COACH BRIAN WILLIAMS

Edited by
LISA LUKE EASTERLING

Edited by
KATHY SWIGLE

Inspired for Life Media

Made to Change the World - Your Life Matters

Small Group Study

Published by: "Inspired for Life Media, Florida"

Proofread and edited by: Lisa Easterling

Manuscript review and contributions by Kathy Swigle

Design ideas: Leslie Quasarano

Design by Tyler Flores

Printed and bound in the United States of America

Visit us on the web at www.madetochangetheworld.com

ABOUT THE AUTHOR

Brian Williams is a double Board-Certified Coach and a Professional Certified Coach (PCC) through the International Coaching Federation. He has coached thousands of people and has led a staff of coaches whose combined efforts have positively impacted the lives of hundreds of thousands.

Brian has extensive experience in helping people improve key areas of their lives including wellness, career, business, relationships, and most importantly, walking with Jesus. He has helped them fulfill their God-ordained purpose through the direction of Jesus Christ. He partners with each person to help him or her clearly move forward by taking the right steps, and, through accountability and encouragement, to achieve those goals.

Brian is also an ordained pastor through the Anchor Bay Evangelistic Association. He uses his spiritual background and training to help others grow through coaching, and has helped lead prayer ministries, facilitate small groups, and organize various spiritual campaigns and church projects. Brian, along with his wife Claudia and their daughter Ellie, attend and serve at FishHawk Fellowship Church in Lithia, Florida.

f

MORE BOOKS AND RESOURCES BY COACH BRIAN WILLIAMS

Am I Saved?

Many Christians walk through life uncertain of their salvation, associating being saved with their own efforts rather than seeing it as a gift of God's grace. This book provides a solid answer to this vital question.

Available on Amazon

Made to Change the World - Your Life Matters

This book will encourage you to know God's calling then provide the tools to live it in every area of your life with an impact that will change the world around you.

Available on Amazon

Made to Change the World - Your Life Matters, Small Group Study

This eight-week study not only walks your group through how to understand God's calling but also provides the way to change and live it out.

Available on Amazon

Walk With God Today

Grow closer to God through this daily devotional that will not only challenge you to think deeper in your faith but to make the changes in your life in order to walk closer with God each day.

Available on Amazon

Directions for Life

If you want to know the purpose, mission, and vision God has for your life and you also want to live it, this is the book for you. This is the starting point to following the call God has for you each day of your life.

Available on Amazon

Lifewise - How to Live by God's Wisdom

One book of the Bible clearly talks about how to be successful, God's way, in every area of life. This book will not only explore what God says but also show you how to live it out.

Talk Truth to Yourself

We easily get off track in life because we believe things that are not true about God and His promises. This book will teach you how to know and to live the truth to receive God's promises.

Available on Amazon

Life Balance for Christians - It's Not What You Think

Balanced living in God's eyes isn't the same as what the world considers balance. More importantly than us figuring out how to balance our own lives, it is surrendering each area to God.

Available on Amazon

Theology of Behavior Change

Many Christians want to change areas in their life or follow God more closely in faith, but do not know how to make changes that last. This book explains how to change and gives supporting tools.

Available at madetochangetheworld.com

For all of these books as well as additional resources to help you fully live the life God desires for you and impact the world around you, go to: www.madetochangetheworld.com. Make sure to watch the short video on our home page and to register to get free weekly emails with videos, tools, and encouragement to support you in your walk with God.

Pastors and Ministry Leaders – See "Ministry Tools" tab at our website www.madetochangetheworld.com for resources to help you disciple those you lead.

CONTENTS

Preface   ix
How To Use This Book   xi
Do You Know Jesus?   xiii
Acknowledgments   xix
Getting Started   xxi
Introduction   xxvii

Session 1   1
Perspective
Session 2   8
Purpose
Session 3   16
Truth and Faith
Session 4   24
Change and Balance
Session 5   35
Action and Self-control
Session 6   47
Perseverance
Session 7   57
Energy
Session 8   68
Celebration

Christian Surrender Wheel   79
Faith Goals Tool   83
Small Group Prayer List   85
How to Use the Weekly Check-in   87
Weekly Check-in Balance Wheel   89

PREFACE

IMPORTANT!

This small group study is designed to be used in conjunction with the *Made to Change the World-Your Life Matters* book by Brian Williams. Using these two books together can be transformational for your life based on how you want to use them.

At a minimum, this study will get you thinking about the importance of your life, your walk with God, and how you live today in light of eternity. It will cause you to think about how you are living and thinking, and whether or not you are having the great adventure and fulfilled life Jesus Christ has planned for you.

At its most effective level, the study will cause you to look deeply into the core of who you are and who God is, and it will transform your thinking and your life as you walk day by day, step by step, and moment by moment with Him. This will lead you to the greatest adventure of your life and also an eternity with many others whom you have impacted and touched along the way for the sake of Jesus.

My background of helping others through hands-on coaching, mentoring, and teaching has prepared me for the writing of both the book and this study. I personally have made big shifts and changes in my own life and thinking as led by God. I have been blessed by the opportunity to help a great number of others change their lives as well. Through all this, I realized we are all exactly the same. At the core of each of us is the desire to be loved, to know God, and to fulfill His purpose. Unfortunately, many people-- including Christians--don't live or experience these things fully in their own lives. I am here to say that you can and you will if you are steadfast in your pursuit of God and His purpose for your life. I have provided some help and support through this study to lead you to achieve just that.

It is important to understand that living fully for Christ does not mean your life will be free of challenges, obstacles, or even difficult situations. It does mean that you will have success (the way God defines it). You will also have complete fulfillment and incredible adventure. The greatest news of all is that you will have the opportunity at the end of your life to hear your Lord and Father, the creator of the universe, say, "Well done, good and faithful servant!"

I believe that if you live a life fully devoted to God by knowing Him, following Him, and living according to His purpose, He will use you in mighty ways. Your life will not only be fulfilling, but will change the world by impacting the people around you.

HOW TO USE THIS BOOK

Through the process of writing *Made to Change the World-Your Life Matters,* many other tools, books, and resources were developed and this small group study guide is one of them. The original book idea morphed into a full life-change program. Depending on the level that you want to be involved and walk more closely with God, this small group study and other tools will help you do so. The goal of this book and all that goes with it is not just to help you learn something new and get excited about life. The goal is to literally help you change who you are, in every area of life, to fully live for God so that you may receive all His promises and fulfill His purpose. In the process, you will change the world around you.

This book is designed and recommended to be used with the *Made to Change the World* book. The best way to grow and change is to partner with someone through this as you read the book each week and work through the sessions together. Below is a description of how to use these two books together so you absorb and put into practice what you learn. I challenge you to not only read this book, but to live it. To get the maximum use out of the *Made to Change the World* book, small group study, and program, do these things as you get ready to start.

Step 1 – Go to www.madetochangetheworld.com and register for free weekly emails that contain videos, tools, and support to help you grow and change.

Step 2 – Set up a weekly day and time to meet with your small group to go through this study together. I recommend meeting for an hour and a half each time, but one hour could also work.

Step 3 – Determine when and where you will meet. Make sure you have a way to watch the video for each week at www.-madetochangetheworld.com. There are many ways to do this, such as using a Smart TV, laptop, iPad, cast to a TV from your phone, etc.

Step 4 – Follow the weekly study layout each week as you grow together in your small group.

Step 5 – Look into additional books, tools, and support provided through the *Made to Change the World* program. These options include memberships, workbooks, and the Change the World Christian Coaching certification.

It is also important to note that *Made to Change the World* is not designed to teach you to fly solo through life. It is designed to help you grow in your relationships with God and others. I strongly encourage you to ask others to walk with you through these changes. As the Bible says, "Man sharpens man like iron sharpens iron," which applies equally to men and women. A word of caution here: it is highly recommended that you have a same-sex accountability partner unless, of course, that person is your spouse or another family member.

Take *Made to Change the World* as a challenge to not only change your own life, but the lives of those around you by fully living your purpose. Jesus said that we would do greater works than He did so here is a very important question to consider: why aren't we each doing these greater works right now? Consider that question as you read and realize that your life matters. You were made to change the world!

DO YOU KNOW JESUS?

This book will be a great help for your walk with Jesus. However, I realize some of you reading this may not know what it means to be a Christian or even if you are one. This section is for you and will help you not only understand what being a Christian means but also help you make the most important decision in your life if you are ready.

I will start with my background and how I became a Christian. In my early 20's, I graduated from college and moved to Florida. Even though I was already becoming successful at a young age, I found myself on Clearwater Beach one Saturday in a miserable state of mind. Even though I had grown up going to church, I ended up hopeless and all the accomplishments, friends, church sermons, and other things I had experienced in life did not bring fulfillment. I asked myself what the purpose was in continuing to move forward in life.

When I got to my lowest low and sat on the beach that day, I looked around at the sky, the ocean, and the birds flying and realized that no man made what I saw and no man controls it. I knew I couldn't make it on my own and needed a bigger purpose and reason for life. I also knew what it meant to turn my life over to God, so I prayed to Jesus and surrendered my life to Him. I knew that I had sinned (missed the mark) many times in my life and asked Jesus to forgive me. I asked Jesus to give me His purpose and direction. I committed to pray and read the Bible every day and promised God that if He would help me out of my miserable mess, I would tell everyone I could about His love and forgiveness and about the transformation in my life. So here I am, writing this to you because of this complete transformation of my life.

I have kept that commitment to spend daily time with Him each morning over the past 20 years. I can probably count on one hand the number of times I have missed praying and Bible reading. There were some big changes God walked me through over the months and years that followed my day at the beach, including putting away my selfish desires, changing my focus, and realigning my thinking in order to believe what is true based on what He says in the Bible. He empowers me to pursue a much bigger and more important purpose for my life here on earth and for eternity.

I have talked with many people and it is easy to see that what the Bible says is true – we all are in the same boat of having sinned in our lives. Sin is the opposite of God's will and is mainly formed from our selfish desires and attitudes. Sin includes things like anger, jealousy, bitterness, fear, unbelieving, immoral thoughts, sexuality outside of marriage, lying, wanting someone else's property, and lust, just to name a few. It is putting yourself and "things" in life as the most important in the place of God. Sin is disobedience to God and not living the way he wants us to live, which is to work together here on this earth through His love.

God not only has a plan for you here on earth, but also for eternity. The problem is that sin separates us from God and causes a chasm between us. This is a chasm we cannot cross on our own because we are the ones who caused it. You may know that in the Old Testament of the Bible, God required people to sacrifice animals to redeem their sins and bridge that chasm. That may sound harsh, but sin is so serious to God that its penalty is death. The payment for sin requires either our own personal death or the death of a substitute.

The great news is that a couple thousand years ago, God made a cataclysmic change by redeeming our sins and removing the separation from Him. He Himself, in the form of His Son, Jesus, came to earth as a baby through a virgin named Mary. This is the real reason we celebrate Christmas. The story doesn't end there, however.

After Jesus was born, He walked the earth and was the only person to live a sinless life and follow God's purpose in every way. At 33 years old, Jesus was put to death. For more details of the amazing life and events of Jesus' life, you can read the books of Matthew, Mark, Luke, and John in the Bible.

Because of Jesus' life and death on the cross, He became the ultimate sacrifice and redemption for our sin. The most exciting part is three days later Jesus rose from the dead and was seen by hundreds of witnesses who not only saw Him, but also talked with Him and even touched his wounds. Jesus did not just die, as have many other religious leaders who are still dead. He rose again and is alive today calling you to Him.

Jesus gave us a way to be forgiven through His sinless blood shed on a cross: He died in our place. You may be familiar with John 3:16, which says, "For God so loved the world that He gave His only son so that whoever believes in Him will not perish but will have eternal life." Another verse in Romans 10 says, "If you declare with your mouth, 'Jesus is Lord', and believe in your heart that God raised him from the dead, you will be saved. For it is with your heart that you believe and are justified, and it is with your mouth that you profess your faith and are saved."

This means that the most incredible thing God could ever do for you, He already did. This means that you don't have to try to face life on your own anymore, but that you will be given a purpose and peace that you can never get anywhere else. It means that you want Him to lead and guide your life. It also means you want to (and will) be with Him for eternity once you leave this earth. In order to bridge that chasm and have a relationship with your heavenly Father, all you have to do is believe. Believe that He died on the cross for you and ask Him to forgive your sins, which again are all the past things you have done wrong in your life. When you ask Him to come into your heart, He will, and He will change your life forever.

If you are ready to turn things over to God and live a full and adventurous life filled with peace and tremendous purpose for now and eternity, here is a prayer for you to pray out loud or in your heart.

"Jesus, I believe you are the son of God and that you died for my sins, then rose again. Thank you for loving me so much that you sacrificed your very life. I know that I have done things in my life that were against your will and purpose. Please forgive me. I want to start new with you! I ask you to come into my life and lead me. I want you to show me your way and the true purpose that you put me on this earth. Thank you, Lord Jesus. I dedicate my life to you. Amen."

Congratulations!

You probably didn't have fireworks go off or hear a voice come down from heaven. You may not have felt anything inside, either, but rest assured that God heard you and He is faithful. What you will probably notice right away, but certainly over time, is a peace inside your heart. You are now part of the family of God, which is a huge family of other believers you will be with for eternity.

It is important to share with someone the decision you made today. You can share it with family or friends. If you have another Christian in your life, I'm sure he or she would love to hear about your decision and so would I. Please email me at hello@madetochangetheworld.com.

A next great step for you would be to attend a local church and/or Bible study group. Make sure the place you attend is using only the Holy Bible as their source of truth and training. Another book to help you more clearly understand salvation and next steps is free for you at my website or on Amazon. It is titled *Am I Saved?* Get your copy by clicking on the Resource tab at www.madetochangetheworld.com.

Now, you may have read all of this and not feel ready to make this change or commitment. I want you to know that God loves you more than you can comprehend! He is faithful and will keep tugging at your heart! If you have questions or need help sorting this out, please email me at hello@madetochangetheworld.com. You may also find great answers and insight by reading the book listed above or *The Case for Christ* by Lee Strobel.

God bless you! Remember that Jesus loves you so much that He died for you.

ACKNOWLEDGMENTS

If you have read any of my testimonial above, you will quickly see I would not even be alive today if Jesus Christ had not saved and changed me. Without Christ's perfect will and plan I would not be here to write a book about how He has impacted my life. Thank you, Lord, for saving me through your mercy and grace on the beach that day and for daily leading me along your path through your Holy Spirit.

I would also be completely remiss if I did not thank my wife Claudia and my little Ellie. They are the most amazing two women I could ask to live my life with. Thank you both for allowing me to spend time writing and helping others during my many busy mornings of book writing.

I am also in complete debt to some others who have been rocks in my life. They have helped me through the tough times, encouraged me with their words, and lifted me up with prayers through this book writing process.

Kathy Swigle is my MTCTW partner and is a gift from heaven. Thank you, Kathy, for sticking with me and for all that you do to change the world every day. She also helped me lay the foundation of this study and did an amazing job helping get this project started.

Leslie Quasarano is an amazing sister in Christ and Coach, and was the first person to head up a Made to Change the World small group study. Thank you, Leslie, to you and your small groups. I am forever grateful.

There are so many others I would like to thank and acknowledge by name but that would turn this into an encyclopedia instead of one book. So I say, "Thank you" from the bottom of my heart to my family and many friends who have supported me, encouraged me, and given me feedback over the years. Thank you also for my church family and my men's group. I especially want to thank the Change the World Coaches, who had great input as I wrote this book and program because they are experts at actually helping others grow and change.

GETTING STARTED

Here is a checklist to help you get started with your *Made to Change the World* small group study:

Organizing your small group meeting:

- *Get a small group of people together to meet*

Ideally, your group size is 4-8 people and in some cases can be a little smaller or larger.

- *Determine a day and time you will meet*

- *Determine where you will meet*

You can continue to meet in the same location every week or change locations as long as everyone in the group is aware of where to join.

- *Determine who will be the host*

The host can be the person who has the group at their home and/or be the person or organizes meeting locations, activities, food/snacks, etc. As a side note, some groups do like to have refreshments. This is a great way to socialize, but make sure it doesn't take away from study time.

- *Determine who will be the facilitator*

The leader is the person who will facilitate the small group discussion. The leader can be the same person as the host or a different person. You can also change leaders from week to week, and even if you keep the same leader, it is important to have a backup in case that person is out.

Group facilitator:

- *Qualifications of a Small Group Leader*

The only qualification is to love Jesus and love others. There is no perfect leader, just someone who is willing to step up and follow God to lead the group.

- *Responsibilities of a Small Group Leader*

The main responsibilities of the small group leader are to:

1) Come to the group prepared, which means being one week ahead in the study. Prior to the group meeting, you should have read the chapter(s), watched the video, and looked over the small group study.

2) Pray for the group members on a weekly basis. You will most likely have prayer requests that come up and as the leader, praying for those requests during your own personal time with God is important.

3) Love others. Every person in the group will be in a different spot in life, facing different struggles and having different levels of faith. In all that you do as a small group leader, help every person know that s/he is loved by God, has a God-given purpose, and will be helped by God.

4) Do the best you can to live your faith, set an example, and be real. No one is perfect. Be yourself and encourage others to do the same as you work together.

- *Keep the group on track:*

Be mindful of time. Work hard to start and end the meeting on time. There may be those who have childcare, etc. If your group together decides to start later or go longer and everyone agrees, then flex as the group desires to flex. Some of these sections could go for several hours if desired, so gauge the group and accomplish the key questions each week. There are suggested time guidelines for each section within the study, but feel free to be flexible. If the group desires to delve deeper or extend the length of the meetings, then do so if everyone is in agreement. Be sensitive to those who have to start and leave at a certain time.

- *Help others grow*

This study is not only designed to help your group to learn, but also to change and grow closer in their walk with God. Make sure as you start each new week by following up on goals, action steps, and commitments made by your group members the week before.

- *Behavior Change Theology*

Optional: Before your group starts, read *The Theology of Behavior Change* located under the "Ministry Tools" tab at madetochangetheworld.com. If you are the ministry leader of your small group, reading this would be quite helpful as you help your group members grow and make changes in their own lives.

- *Read "How to Use This Book"*

You will find at the beginning of this book a "How to Use This Book" section. It is important that you read that couple of pages, and encourage your group members to read them as well.

Host Home:

- *Have a space where people can sit*

In order to host a small group at your house, you do not need a big home. As a matter of fact, smaller homes can bring people closer together. You just have to be willing to open your heart and home and have an area where people can sit, ideally in a circle or semicircle type formation., and interact. It is also important that there is some way to play/watch the weekly videos. For tips on this, go to the "How to Use this Book" section of the book.

- *Let people know where things are located in the house*

When people first come to your home, it is important to let them know where you will meet, locations of bathrooms, etc. You want them to feel comfortable getting around.

- *Babysitting*

Some groups are made up of young families and will have a babysitter in the home during the time of the small group. If this is something your group would like to do, determine who will be babysitting each week. You could take turns doing this or bring someone else in to help. You will also need to have a room designated for childcare.

- *Group host.*

You opening your home for the group does not necessarily mean you have to be the group host. The host helps organize things, including times and dates to meet, food, etc.

Virtual Group Hosting:

- If you will be leading a virtual group meeting, send an email to all the participants with the pertinent details (meeting link, video links, session prep information, phone #'s to call if needed for troubleshooting) ahead of time.

- Small group videos and session notes can be found at madetochangetheworld.com/videos. The password is (all lower case): **mtctwvideos**

INTRODUCTION

Thank you for being interested in going through the *Made to Change the World* Small Group Study and willing to grow closer in your walk with God. This small group study is designed to be used with the *Made to Change the World* book. I hope and pray that as you go through this study, you will grow closer to those in your group and, most importantly, closer to God!

God has tremendous purpose for you. This study will help you not only to realize that purpose, but to walk in His truth and help change the world around you. The more willing and open you are to let God stretch you and grow your faith, the greater the walk you will have with Jesus.

Here is how the weekly group sessions are laid out:

1. Meet together for 8 weeks/sessions
2. Open with prayer each week
3. Discuss what has happened in your walk with God since the last meeting

4. Watch the current week video (if meeting virtually, you may want to have members watch video prior to meeting)
5. Discuss the current week content
6. Set your intention for the week
7. End in prayer and social time as desired

Have a great time getting to know each other, growing together, and walking with Jesus. I would love to have you share how your group is going by emailing me at hello@madetochangetheworld.com

SESSION 1
PERSPECTIVE

As you get started together in this new small group study, it is important to realize that no one in your group is perfect and trust and love are the priority. As you love God more, you will learn to love and support each other as well.

Before jumping into the study right away, start with getting to know each other a little bit more. Whether this is your first time meeting all together or your small group has been going for many years, take one of the following questions and each take turns answering before moving on.

1. What is the toughest thing for you in knowing/following God?
2. If you got a million-dollar check handed to you right now, how would you spend it?
3. Finish this sentence: If I were a Bible character, I would be _____ because...

The ultimate purpose of this study is:

1. To live a faithful, impactful, and adventurous life for Christ
2. To **Change the World** around you as you live out Purpose #1

Key areas of intended learning and growth this week from this study:

- Realize your impact on this world
- Desire to live fully for God in every area of life
- By faith, take action and "do something" to impact the world around you

I] *Prayer Requests/ Praise Reports and Prayer*

Turn to the back of this book for the section to write down your group's prayer requests, then refer to it through the week to pray for your group members.

Main Scripture

Matthew 4:19-20 – "'Come, follow me,' Jesus said, 'and I will send you out to fish for people.' At once they left their nets and followed him."

II] Overview of the topic & video

This session will lead you to discuss what it means to be saved. It will also cause you to think and act differently based on that decision. If you call yourself a Christian, you must believe in God's Word and His truth for your life. He made you for a reason, and as you follow Him and live out His purpose, it will change this world. This session is based on Chapters 1 and 2 of the *Made to Change the World* book, which is recommended reading in conjunction with this study.

Small group videos and session notes can be found at madetochangetheworld.com / videos. The password is (all lower case): **mtctwvideos**

Watch Small Group Introduction & Session 1 Videos

- Meet Coach Brian Williams

- What inspired me to write MTCTW
- Jerome and the wake-up call
- Peter, Jesus, and the Call
- YOU are here to change the world
- Your beliefs about who you are - are they true or not?

III] Powerful Questions to Discuss as a Group

Like Jerome, if you knew your reason for living, how would that change you?

- What does "being saved" mean to you?
- What is something you would like to change in your life to draw closer to God and experience His love?
- Since you are made to be uniquely you, what abilities and gifts do you have?
- How do you invest time and energy in developing your talents?
- Think of 3 people by name who are around you on a regular basis. In what ways is God calling you to love each of these people?

IV] GOING DEEPER

Take two minutes to read the following and then discuss it

Ben was in his early 20's when I met him and was confined to an electric wheelchair. He couldn't move his legs at all. He could move his arms enough to control the electric joystick on his wheelchair to move around. He couldn't move his head much, but he could talk and smile, and that he did. He was a huge Florida Gators fan, so his dog who accompanied him always had on a Gator bandana and Ben went to many of the games. Ben was always encouraging.

What was most impressive about Ben was that he was going to school to design racing wheelchairs. He loved the idea of faster and more mobile chairs and decided to do something about it to help him and all those who are wheelchair-bound. He believed he was made to change the world and not just accept the hand he was dealt with tears and a "feel sorry for me" attitude.

Ben died a couple of years after we met. I am not sure how far he came along with designing his wheelchair, but it doesn't matter. His life encouraged me and many others around him to live bigger, believe more, and do all we can each day. His smile, attitude, and motivation changed me and I realized that if I can actually walk, move, and live longer, I have an even bigger responsibility to live my purpose and to impact this world. As Luke 12:48 says, "To whom much is given, much is required."

 What stands out to you about Ben's story?

Do you know your purpose?

ASSESSMENT

HOW READY ARE YOU TO TAKE ACTION? FIND OUT HERE BY TAKING THIS assessment:

Online Version: https://madetochangetheworld.com/assessment

PLEASE RATE YOUR RESPONSE ON A SCALE FROM 1–10 *	10	9	8	7	6	5	4	3	2	1
I am very satisfied with my life	O	O	O	O	O	O	O	O	O	O
I can clearly identify/articulate what needs changed in the world	O	O	O	O	O	O	O	O	O	O
I am actively making changes in the areas I feel passionate about changing	O	O	O	O	O	O	O	O	O	O
I am influential with others	O	O	O	O	O	O	O	O	O	O
I have a set of core values that guide my life	O	O	O	O	O	O	O	O	O	O
I know my purpose for being on this earth	O	O	O	O	O	O	O	O	O	O
I regularly set and achieve goals to achieve my purpose	O	O	O	O	O	O	O	O	O	O
I live a balanced life that keeps me on track	O	O	O	O	O	O	O	O	O	O
I have support in my life that keeps me going on the right path	O	O	O	O	O	O	O	O	O	O
I have high energy to help me impact this world	O	O	O	O	O	O	O	O	O	O

What is your score?

Rubric for assessment

- 90-100: You are living your life with purpose.

- 80-90: You have knowledge about your purpose.

- 70-80: You could benefit from being clearer and more focused on your purpose.

- 60-70: What is a purpose statement?

What does your result mean to you?

The Three Things

The way you live your life as a Christian each day comes down to three things:

1) What you know about God and the power He has given you on this earth

2) Your willingness to accept the truth of God for your own life

3) Your commitment to live full out for God based on faith alone

Do you agree or disagree with these three things? Why or why not?

V] What did I learn and how will I use it? Takeaways:

- My prayer is...

- List any and all things you feel God may be prompting you to work on in your life.

- Pick **ONE** of the things listed above, then finish this sentence: This week, I commit to...

- My action plan to complete my commitment is...

- What exactly will you do?

- How will you do it?

- When will you do it?

- What do you need to change to get this done?

- Who or what can help you get it done (accountability)?

HOW CONFIDENT ARE YOU IN GETTING THIS DONE?

IMPORTANT – Only set an action step you feel very confident you can achieve this next week, even if it seems to be a small first step. There will be a check-in on this next session. Record this goal in the Action Tracker section.

READ THIS CLOSING PRAYER TOGETHER

Lord Jesus, You made the world, then you came to live with us in order to change it! You came to save me and challenge me to also change the world. Help me to think bigger, believe more, and be the person you called me to be. As I live for you, let my life be a light to draw others to you. In Jesus's name, Amen.

NEXT STEPS:

- Complete the action step you listed out above
- Read chapters 1 and 2 in *Made to Change the World* for next week
- Have an accountability partner to talk/pray with before next session

SESSION 2

PURPOSE

Session Focus - from Chapter 1 and 2 of the MTCTW book

- Learn the importance of knowing your life purpose
- Draft a life purpose statement

Catching Up:

Last week, the session covered getting the right perspective about God and who He made you to be. This week you will start with re-connecting through prayer, updating on how you did last week with your goal, and working on your personal purpose statement.

I] Prayer Requests/ Praise Reports and Prayer

Turn to the back of this book for the section to review previous prayer requests, update answers, and add additional requests that are mentioned.

MAIN SCRIPTURE

1 Corinthians 13:13 – "And now these three things remain: faith, hope and love. But the greatest of these is love."

ACCOUNTABILITY

Each group member should look back to their action step from Session 1 in the Spiritual Growth Log, then give a one-minute update to the group on what that goal was and how it went with accomplishing it.

If you completed your step of faith, congratulations! Record it in your Action Tracker (in the Spiritual Growth Log).

If the action step was missed, what is the new plan to be able to reach it this week?

II] OVERVIEW OF THE TOPIC & VIDEO

This session will help you realize that there is a great purpose God has for you on this earth. You are here at His chosen time to fulfill an important calling. However, it is easy to get into the grind of everyday life and miss His direction. When we do our own thing, we not only miss receiving the great promises He has for us, we also miss letting God use us to make an impact on this world.

Small group videos and session notes can be found at madetochangetheworld.com/videos. The password is (all lower case): **mtctwvideos**

WATCH SESSION 2 VIDEO

- Lessons from the Lion King
- Life purpose
- The stadium
- The ripple effect

III] Powerful Questions to Discuss as a Group

- What comes to your mind when you picture that all of heaven celebrated the day you accepted Jesus as your Lord and Savior?
- Do you believe you are here for a purpose?
- How would it change your life if you knew your purpose?
- Who is in your section of the stadium?
- What kind of ripple are you making right now in life and what ripple would you like to make?

IV] Going Deeper

Take two minutes to read the following, then discuss it

The first time I held my daughter, I could not believe that God would trust me with this tiny human life. I remember thinking to myself that I must support her back and head, and, most importantly, to not drop her. *Whatever you do, don't drop her!* My wife even has a picture of that moment with a clear look on my face of "don't drop the baby". Thankfully, I didn't.

I realized that already contained within this tiny baby is everything she will need for her life. She was a brand-new human that would one day grow up to be and do things that only God knows. She was helpless. She was beautiful. She could do absolutely nothing on her own.

The early days were critical for us to get to know her and find what she needs. We had to take care of her. To learn about her needs and tendencies and pay attention to every little thing. It took self-sacrifice and many sleepless nights. At that time, she could give us nothing in return. She was trying to stay alive and figure out this new world.

We did all of these things for our little girl and still do today based on one thing, which is love. Claudia and I love Ellie with all of our hearts, and no matter what she does, we choose to love her and always will. We may not be happy with all the things she does, but our love and caring for her is not based on what she does. It is based on who she is.

Love is our purpose on earth. From the day we were created, and every day after, love is at our core. We were made to love and to be loved. That is God's purpose for you. That is why He made the world: because of love.

- What stands out to you about this story?
- How do you define love?
- How often do you choose to love in your daily life?

Life Purpose Statement

Although we know God's purpose for us is to love, it is important to articulate in your own words the purpose for which you believe God put you here on this earth. The purpose for your life does not change. You may adjust the way you word it over time, but it is stating the reason you are on this earth.

Why do you think God put you on this earth?

A well drafted life purpose statement helps you make life decisions based on that purpose. It is like an anchor for life that as the wind blows and waves rise up, it keeps you connected to the rock, which is Jesus.

How would you describe your relationship with Jesus?

As Zig Ziglar said "you have to be before you can do and you have to do before you can have." The purpose statement is about your "being" (not your doing or your having).

What are a few words to describe who you are according to God's Word?

A life purpose statement is one sentence about who you are. The challenge with writing it is not to express what you will do or what you hope to accomplish but stating who you are. Based on your answers above, take a shot at writing one sentence to describe who you are in God.

Finish this sentence by writing it here: "I am...

Take a few minutes to discuss what you have drafted with the rest of your group. There will be more time for you to focus on this during the week. This practice is a good start.

V] What did I learn and how will I use it? Takeaways:

- My prayer is...

- What, if anything, do you need to continue working on from last week?

- This week focus on not only drafting your purpose statement but also memorizing it and quoting it each morning when you wake up.

- My plan to complete my purpose statement this week is:

- What exactly will you do related to drafting your purpose statement?

- How will you do it?

- When will you do it?

- What do you need to adjust in your schedule to fit this in?

- Who or what can help you get it done (accountability)?

- How confident are you in getting this done?

IMPORTANT – Only set an action step you feel very confident you can achieve this next week. There will be a check-in on it next session. Record this step in the Action Tracker.

Use the Purpose Worksheet below to write your purpose statement during the week. This may take a few attempts so be patient with yourself. Feel free to come back to it during this small group study and revise it along the way. If you would like additional help in writing your purpose, mission, and vision statements, you can purchase the *Directions for Life* book by Brian Williams at www. madetochangetheworld.com.

Read this closing prayer together

Lord Jesus, thank you for loving me always, even when I fail. Thank you for loving me when I am not lovable. Thank you for forgiving me and saving me. I ask that you help me know and live the purpose you have for me. Help me to love those around me with your true love. In Jesus' name, Amen.

Next Steps:

- Complete your action step listed above by using the worksheet below
- Read chapters 3 and 4 in *Made to Change the World* for next week
- Have an accountability partner to talk/pray with before next session

- How much time have you spent reflecting on the purpose of your life?
- Have you ever drafted your own personal "purpose statement"? If so, what is it?

How to write your purpose statement worksheet:

Step 1 – Set aside time to draft your Purpose Statement:

Step 2 – Meditate on Scriptures that relate to God's purpose for you:

1 Corinthians 13:4-8, Galatians 5:22-23, 2 Peter 1:5-11, Romans 8:1-39, Proverbs 3:1-35

- What are the keywords that stand out to you from reading these Scriptures?
- Why do they stand out to you?
- What are the common themes of these words and attributes?

Step 3 – What is most important to you in life and why?

- Write down your answers to what is most important in your life and why.

Step 4 – Spiritual beliefs and views of eternity

- Write down a few sentences that describe your belief in God and your view of eternity:

Step 5– Beginning to draft your Purpose Statement

- "What is most important in my life?" "Why is that so important to me?"

Step 6–Refining your priority list

- Write down four words or adjectives that would describe the

most meaningful life you could live for God (you can start
with 8 or 10 then start narrowing it down).

- Write each word out on index cards then lay them out in front
  of you. Pick the absolute highest priority card first, second,
  next, and so forth until you get all four in priority order.

Step 7–First draft of you your Purpose Statement:

- Look for common themes, ideas, and driving factors from what
  you listed above.
- Draft your own personal purpose statement (use up to three
  sentences):

Step 8–Fine-tuning your Purpose Statement:

- Take the most powerful pieces of what you drafted and
  condense it into one sentence.

Step 9 – Drafting your Purpose Statement:

- Does what you drafted for your purpose statement give you: 1)
  energy and 2) focus when you read it? If so, congratulations!
- If not, keep fine-tuning it over the days and weeks until it "hits
  the spot".
- Once you have the Purpose Statement the way you want it,
  memorize it and repeat it each morning.

Step 10–Live it

- Find support to help you focus on and fulfill your life purpose.

SESSION 3
TRUTH AND FAITH

S ession Focus - from Chapters 3 and 4 of the MTCTW book

- Define Truth and live by it more each day
- Become bolder and more confident in your faith

Catching Up:

Last week, Session Two covered purpose in life. Hopefully, you had a chance to at least draft a purpose statement that is worded in a way that grounds you in the truth of who God made you to be and gets you excited about living it out. If you didn't get to do this or it's not quite where you want it to be, keep working on it and begin to quote it every day.

This session is going to cover two powerful and life-changing topics that work closely together. The first is truly knowing and believing God's truth and the second is how to live by faith in God's truth. These two things together will change your life and cause you to change the world.

I] Prayer Requests/ Praise Reports and Prayer

Turn to the back of this book for the section to review previous prayer requests, update answers to prayers, and add additional requests that are mentioned.

Main Scripture

2 Timothy 2:15 – "Do your best to present yourself to God as one approved, a worker who does not need to be ashamed, and who correctly handles the word of truth."

Accountability

Each group member should look in the Spiritual Growth Log at their action step from Session 2 related to drafting a personal purpose statement. Go around and give a one-minute update to the group on how you did with your step as well as anything you are still working on from Session 1.

If you completed your step, congratulations! Record it in your Action Tracker.

If the step of faith was missed, what is the new plan to be able to reach it this week?

A key point to consider is that if you get behind with your action steps, complete the original ones first and it is really only good to work on 1-2 goals at a time. More than that will easily get you stuck.

II] Overview of the topic & video

This session will help you learn to live by the Truth of God's word. You will have the opportunity to implement the 10 Truths into your life. During this session, you will also learn what it means to live from truth and faith instead of from false beliefs and fear. This session will help you become more confident in your faith because you serve a faithful God.

Small group videos and session notes can be found at madetochangetheworld.com/videos. The password is (all lower case): **mtctwvideos**

· · ·

WATCH SESSION 3 VIDEO

- The One Question
- 10 Things that are true about you
- Faith vs. Fear
- Choose wisely

III] A Powerful Question to Discuss as a Group

Read the following excerpt from the MTCTW book, then discuss the one question:

As I was at the conference, I wondered why this wise and experienced group could not find the truth and think about God in the midst of so many philosophies, religions, and personal desires. Then it hit me. There is really only one question each of us needs to answer to determine what we will believe in life and if we will help change the world for God's purpose.

The foundational question is: '**Do you believe Jesus is alive today?**' Nearly everyone and all other religions believe Jesus lived. Many even believe He did great things and performed miracles. Most people believe He was a great prophet and had much wisdom to offer. However, if Jesus actually did all these things, died, and came back to life three days later, then He really must be the Son of God and He REALLY did change the world!

There are hundreds if not thousands of prophets and wise people through history on whom we could base our hope and future, including Muhammad and Buddha. However, all of these men, women, and others have since died (or will die if still living). They could not save themselves from death. This is not to take away from some of the wisdom they had for life, but ultimately, they could not save themselves so you cannot trust they will save you or anyone else for the afterlife.

The only "prophet" who died, was three days in the grave, then rose again to life is Jesus (according to the Bible and other sources). If He is the only one actually still alive today, overcoming death, then He is the only one we can trust with our lives on earth and for eternity. The question then becomes for each of us, "Do I believe Jesus is alive?

Based on your answer, your future then becomes simple. If you do not believe Jesus existed or rose from the dead, then you are really free to pick whatever "truth" or prophet you want to follow, because they all ended up in the same place – six feet under. The belief you choose will also be the extent of your impact on this world. If, however, Jesus did rise and is alive today, then your only option is to believe Jesus to be who He claims to be (the Son of God) and what is taught in the Bible.

Based on this one question, how would you describe what you believe?

IV] Going Deeper

Take two minutes to read the following and discuss

Truth 1 – **God formed you.**

Psalm 139:13 (NLT) – "You made all the delicate, inner parts of my body and knit me together in my mother's womb."

Truth 2 – **God knows you.**

John 10:14 (ESV) – "I am the good shepherd. I know my own and my own know me."

Truth 3 – **God loves you!**

Romans 5:8 (NIV) – "God shows His love for us in that while we were still sinners, Christ died for us."

Truth 4 – **God has a plan for you.**

Jeremiah 29:11 (NIV) – "'For I know the plans I have for you', declares the Lord, 'plans to prosper you and not to harm you. Plans to give you hope and a future.'"

Truth 5 – **YOU must choose to serve the Lord (or not).**

Joshua 24:15 (KJV) – "… Choose you this day whom you will serve…"

Truth 6 – **You are God's workmanship.**

Ephesians 2:10 (MSG) – "He creates each of us by Christ Jesus to join Him in the work he does, the good work he has gotten ready for us to do, work we should be doing."

Truth 7 – **You have the power of God at work in you.**

Ephesians 3:20 (NIV) – "Now to Him who is able to do immeasurably more than all we ask or imagine, according to His power that is at work within us..."

Truth 8 – **You must have faith.**

Hebrews 11:6a (AMP) – "But without faith, it is impossible to (walk with God and) please Him…"

Truth 9 – **You must grow and mature.**

2 Peter 1:5-8 (NIV) – "For this very reason, make every effort to add to your faith goodness; and to goodness, knowledge; and to knowledge, self-control; and to self-control, perseverance; and to perseverance, godliness, and to godliness, mutual affection; and to mutual affection, love. For if you possess these qualities in increasing measure, they will keep you from being ineffective and unproductive in your knowledge of the Lord Jesus Christ."

Truth 10 – **You will do greater things as you follow Jesus.**

John 14:12 (NIV) – "Very truly I tell you, whoever believes in me will do the works I have been doing, and they will do even greater things than these because I am going to the Father. And I will do whatever you ask in my name so that the Father may be glorified through the Son."

Powerful Questions

- What is your personal statement of faith?

- How do you know what is true?

- Out of the 10 truths, which is easiest to believe? Which is the most difficult to accept?

- Review the three types of life situations where we make decisions:

THE THREE SITUATIONS ARE:

- Decisions that are clear based on God's word (i.e. 10 Commandments, etc)
- Decisions that are situational (i.e. drinking alcohol, etc.)
- Decisions that are not spelled out in the Bible such as a new job offer.

HOW DO YOU KNOW WHAT GOD IS SAYING TO YOU IN EACH ONE?

V] *What did I learn and how will I use it? Takeaways:*

- My prayer is...

- What, if anything, do you need to continue working on from last week?

- This week's focus is on knowing and believing the truth. Take time and read through each one of the ten truths and ask yourself if you believe each one of them enough to base your life on it. If you struggle with any of the truths, make a plan for how to start trusting Jesus and His truth completely for every area of your life.

- Make a specific plan to more genuinely live according to God's truth this week by answering the following questions:

- What exactly will you do to focus on and believe in God's truth?

- How will you do it?

- When will you do it?

- What do you need to adjust in order to make this change?

- Who or what can help you get it done (accountability)?

- How confident are you in getting this done?

IMPORTANT REMINDER 1 – Only set an action step you feel very confident you can achieve this next week. There will be a check-in during the next session.

IMPORTANT REMINDER 2 – Don't forget to record this step in the Action Tracker.

Read this closing prayer together

Lord Jesus, you are the way, the truth, and the life. No one comes to the Father except through you. I come to you and lay down my life, my thoughts, and all that I am. Show me your way and your truth. Set me free from the false beliefs in this world and help me to live by your truth alone. I surrender all to you and ask you to strip away any lies I believe. Replace them with your truth. I ask this in Jesus' name. Amen.

Next Steps:

- Complete your action step listed above

- Read chapters 4 and 5 in Made to Change the World for next week

- Have an accountability partner to talk/pray with before next session

SESSION 4
CHANGE AND BALANCE

S ession Focus - from Chapters 5 and 6 of the MTCTW book

- Learn how to make changes in your life to follow God
- Explore what changes God may be calling you to make

Catching Up:

Last week's Session 3 covered how to know the truth of God and live according to it. Hopefully, you were able to recognize the areas in your life that you are living by God's truth. You may also have discovered areas where you need to improve. How did it go with the area you were working on? If you didn't get to make all the progress you desired, keep working on it and have someone in the group support you as you make these changes.

This session is going to cover two powerful and life-changing topics that work closely together. The first is understanding how we actually change areas of our life and the other is having balance in life according to God's design. These two things together, combined with what you have already been working on, will change your life and ultimately cause you to change the world.

. . .

I] PRAYER REQUESTS/ PRAISE REPORTS AND PRAYER

Turn to the back of this book for the section to review previous prayer requests, update answers to prayers, and add additional requests that are mentioned.

Main Scripture

Proverbs 16:3 (NIV) – "Commit to the Lord whatever you do, and He will establish your plans."

ACCOUNTABILITY

Each group member should look in the Spiritual Growth Log at their action step from Session 3 related to believing and living God's Truth for your life. Go around and give a one-minute update to the group on how you did with your goal as well as anything you are still working on from previous sessions.

If you completed your step, congratulations! Record it in your Action Tracker.

If the action step was missed, what is the new plan to be able to reach it this week?

A key point to consider is that if you get behind with your action steps, complete the original ones first. Also, it is good to only work on 1-2 actions at a time. More than that will easily get you stuck.

II] Overview of the topic & video

In this session, you will learn the importance of changing whatever is holding you back from following Christ fully because anything that is not aligned with God's will pulls you down. During this session, you will learn about the change process, how to make plans to move forward, and what it means to commit to action. There are various areas of your life that need to be balanced and surrendered and you will learn to use a new tool called the *Surrender Wheel* to help you do just that.

Small group videos and session notes can be found at madetochangetheworld.com/videos. The password is (all lower case): **mtctwvideos**

WATCH SESSION 4 VIDEO

- Logic, will, and emotions
- How they work together as we make decisions
- Why change is hard
- How to make changes in your life
- The Surrender Wheel

III] POWERFUL QUESTIONS TO DISCUSS AS A GROUP

- What behavior God is leading you to change?
- From the progression steps listed below, in what step are you in changing the area God is showing you and why?
- Awareness (I just became aware of this and am considering it)
- Thinking (I am still determining what this area of change really means)
- Feelings (I am starting to feel an emotional drive to make this change)
- Will (I am determined to make a change)
- Decision (I choose to make a change in this area)
- Commitment (I am committing to make this change)
- Plan (I am making a plan to enact in order to make this change)
- Accountable (I have someone to hold me accountable to my plan for change)
- Who are 3 people you could rely upon for supportive accountability when you are ready to change a behavior?

IV] Going Deeper

The Christian Surrender Wheel is a tool to help you know how you are doing in all the areas of your life where God calls you to take responsibility. The wheel is very unique in that the question to ask for each spoke of the wheel is not how well you are specifically performing in that area, but how well you have surrendered that area over to God in your life.

For example, looking at the family spoke in your wheel. If you have a family (considering spouse, kids, parents, siblings, etc.), how much do you ask God to lead you in how to relate with them and love them? Additionally, how well do you follow what God shows you in this area through His Word and prayer. If you feel that most of the time you are seeking God about your family, hearing His direction, and doing those things, you may give yourself an eight or nine.

A word to the wise. This wheel is not to condemn you, but instead to lift you up. This is the start of where God can show you His plan and His next steps through His power. It is the first place to understand where you are and where God wants you to get to. In the next chapter, I will help you learn ways to actually make changes in the specific area where God is calling you to do so.

Look at the wheel below and then rank yourself in each area based on how much God is leading you in this area of your life.

Take the assessment by ranking 1-10 based on asking God how well you surrender.

1) Spiritual:

2) **Mental:**

3) **Physical:**

4) **Family:**

5) **Relationships:**

6) **Career:**

7) **Finances:**

8) **Recreation:**

TOTAL SCORE:

TAKE A LOOK AT YOUR TOTAL SCORE:

If you scored over 65: You have a good overall balance in surrendering to God.

If you scored under 65: You can probably feel your life is out of balance with God.

What area is the highest? You can probably think of reasons why it is so high.

What area is the lowest? You can probably also think of reasons why it is so low.

HOW ARE YOU DOING WITH THE OUTER CIRCLE OF THE RIM?

1) **Attitude:**

2) **Time:**

3) **Talents:**

TOTAL SCORE:

Under 25: You probably have some things you would like to improve, especially since these areas directly relate to fulfilling your purpose in life. Ask yourself the same questions as those above for the eight areas of the balance wheel.

Have someone in the group read out loud (or take turns reading) the following:

Once you take the assessment by plotting your answers on the wheel, then connect the dots. You will most likely notice you don't have a round, smooth, and perfect wheel. Going back to the example earlier in this chapter, this is currently the wheel you have on your "bike of life". How smooth is your ride? Would you put that on your actual bike today and try to ride on it? It may be a rather jagged wheel and not a very easy ride.

Having all 10's on your Balance Wheel is not the goal. That is neither realistic nor practical. The realistic place to be is 7-9 most of the time in most of the areas. Life happens, we get caught off guard, things come up, and we have to adjust, so a generally larger wheel with decent balance will roll well through life.

One other important note is that you could have a very balanced wheel by having all low numbers, such as 3's, 2's or 1's in your life. The good news is that it rolls. The bad news is that it is so small, it has to roll twice as fast as a normal-sized wheel. It is too small for your life and will quickly burn you out because your efforts are exhausting but ineffective. You will be peddling that "bike of life" so hard that you won't last long since nothing is working as God desires and requires.

Have fun using this tool. Don't put too much pressure on yourself, but do take it seriously. Realize that these things really make up your life and if the hub of your wheel is not centered on God, you have it on the wrong axle and at some point it will fall off.

WHAT DOES THIS WHEEL SHOW YOU ABOUT YOUR LIFE?

WHAT WOULD YOU LIKE THIS WHEEL TO BE LIKE (REALIZING ALL 10'S ALL the time is not realistic)?

WHAT AREA(S) DO YOU FEEL GOD IS SHOWING YOU TO WORK ON?

· · ·

THE HUB

This wheel is a symbol of the parts of life, but the most important thing to understand is what is at the hub or axle of that wheel. A wheel is only as strong as what it is centered upon. For example, if the wheel we have been talking about was a stagecoach wheel, it would carry a lot of weight and people. The Wheel would mean nothing if it was not placed on a solid iron or steel axle. If that axle were not strong, the wheel would easily bend or break, causing injury.

The hub for our wheel of life has to be centered on God in order for us to have any chance of a purposeful, fulfilling and impactful life. Your hub for all your areas of life must be based on the truth and power of God in order to get the blessing and promises of God in every area of your life. Thankfully, God gives us timeless direction in each of these areas on how-to live in order to center our life on the hub of His Truth.

Although the wheel we have been talking about is not literal, it is something visual that can be applied to all areas of life. If you find an area you need to work on, perhaps starting with your weakest spoke, there is a separate wheel focused on that particular area. For instance, in the area of career, there are components that make that one area strong or weak in relation to how God wants you to live it. Once you assess that area, the wheel shows you specifically what to address. You can find these additional area-specific wheels at www. madetochangetheworld.com.

Once God becomes the axle and center of every area of your life and His truth permeates every spoke, He is the force that powers your "wheel of life" and moves you forward.

WHAT IS THE CURRENT HUB OF YOUR LIFE?

WHAT DO YOU WANT THE HUB TO BE?

· · ·

USE THIS TOOL AT LEAST ONCE PER WEEK. PRINT IT OUT AND EVALUATE yourself, then pray for God's wisdom and direction on how to use what you learn. Partner for support with a Coach, mentor, or accountability partner. For additional help in this area you can go to www. madetochangetheworld.com and click the Coaching tab.

V] WHAT DID YOU LEARN AND HOW WILL YOU USE IT? TAKEAWAYS:

- My prayer is...

- What, if anything, do you need to continue working on from last week?

- This week's focus is on surrendering the areas of your life that are not currently surrendered to God so He can lead and bless you in those areas. Pray, then pick the most important area God is calling you to work on first.

- My plan to begin surrendering the most challenging area of my life to God:

- What exactly will you do related to this area you need to surrender?

- How will you do it?

- When will you do it?

- What do you need to adjust in order to make this change?

- Who or what can help you get it done (accountability)?

- How confident are you in getting this done?

IMPORTANT – ONLY SET AN ACTION STEP YOU FEEL VERY CONFIDENT you can achieve it over this next week. There will be a check-in on it next session.

IMPORTANT – Don't forget to record this action step in the Action Tracker.

Each week you will start your group off by filling in the Surrender Wheel based on how the week went and checking in on your goal for the week. Ideally, as your group continues after this study, or even if it ends, continue filling out the Surrender Wheel every week. This will help you to know where God is leading you and to begin making the changes He is asking you to make.

If you would like to know more and grow deeper in the areas where you are needing to change, consider purchasing the book *The Surrender Wheel - Christian Life Balance is Not What You Think* by Coach Brian Williams. This will show you the specific areas of the spoke you are working on to help you to identify what and where to change to glorify God. You can find the surrender wheel book at www. madetochangetheworld.com or on Amazon.

Read this closing prayer together

Lord Jesus, I surrender all the areas of my life to you. Please guide me to change what You want to see changed in my life. Help me to be balanced Your way. Please help me to have a Godly attitude and to use my time and talents effectively for Your glory. I love you, Lord. You created me for a purpose. Help me to know what it is and to live it out daily. I ask this in Jesus' name. Amen.

Next Steps:

- Complete your action steps listed above by using the Christian Life Surrender Wheel
- Read chapters 7 and 8 in *Made to Change the World* for next week
- Have an accountability partner to talk/pray with before next session

SESSION 5

ACTION AND SELF-CONTROL

Session Focus - from Chapters 7 and 8 of the MTCTW book

- Learn how to live a life of God-directed action
- Know where and how God expects you to use self-control

Catching Up:

Last week's Session Four covered how to make changes and have Godly balance in life. Hopefully, you were able to make some new steps in this area. How did it go? Remember that making changes and surrendering to God is a continual process. The goal is not to do it just one time, but to get into a habit of knowing Him, hearing Him, then following by faith as He leads you.

This session is going to cover how to take action in your life and to make sure you have key areas of self-control. Faith is a noun, but it is also a verb indicating action--not only in doing the things God calls us to do, but in avoiding things that are against His holiness.

. . .

I] PRAYER REQUESTS/ PRAISE REPORTS AND PRAYER

Turn to the back of this book for the section to review previous prayer requests, update answers to prayers, and add additional requests that are mentioned.

Main Scripture

Ephesians 3:20 says, "Now to him who is able to do immeasurably more than all we ask or imagine, according to his power that is at work within us..."

Surrender Wheel

Take a minute to fill out the Surrender Wheel based on how things went for you this week and how surrendered you were to God in each area. If you need refreshing on how to use this wheel, refer back to Session 4.

Take the assessment by ranking 1-10 based on asking God how well you surrender.

1) **Spiritual:**

2) **Mental:**

3) **Physical:**

4) **Family:**

5) **Relationships:**

6) **Career:**

7) **Finances:**

8) **Recreation:**

TOTAL SCORE:

TAKE A LOOK AT YOUR TOTAL SCORE:

If you scored over 65: You have a good overall balance in surrendering to God.

If you scored under 65: You can probably feel your life is out of balance with God.

What area is the highest? You can probably think of reasons why it is so high.

What area is the lowest? You can probably also think of reasons why it is so low.

How are you doing with the outer circle of the rim:

1) **Attitude:**

2) **Time:**

3) **Talents:**

TOTAL SCORE:

Under 25: You probably have some things you would like to improve, especially since these areas directly relate to you fulfilling your purpose in life. Ask yourself the same questions as those above for the eight areas of the balance wheel.

Accountability

Group members should look at their Surrender Wheel and Spiritual Growth Log at their action steps from Session 4 related to changing and surrendering everything to God. Go around and give a one-minute update to the group on how you did with your step as well as anything you are still working on from previous sessions.

If you completed your steps, congratulations! Record it in your Action Tracker.

If the action step was missed, what is the new plan to be able to reach it this week (be specific)?

A key point to consider is that if you get behind with your actions, complete the original ones first. It is really only good to work on 1-2 goals at a time. More than that will easily get you stuck.

II] *Overview of the topic & video*

In this session, you will learn that you need to make a choice to go for all God has for you to move forward in faith. You will also learn the importance of being in God's Word, conversing with Him through prayer, and learning ways to follow His direction for your life.

Small group videos and session notes can be found at madetochangetheworld.com/videos. The password is (all lower case): **mtctwvideos**

WATCH SESSION 5 VIDEO

- A Great Surprise for you
- Ephesians 3:20
- Keys to Knowing How God is leading you
- How to follow Him

III] *Powerful Questions to Discuss as a Group*

- What if anything do you need to ask God's forgiveness for?
  Ask Him what you need to change in the way you live.
- What action do you think God wants you to take?

- Are you dedicating time to spend with God and get into His word? If not, what can you do to make time to be with God and listen to His will for you?

IV] Going Deeper

Have someone in the group read out loud (or take turns reading) the following:

In a study done in 2006, it was estimated that about 3% of the population in the United States had written goals. It was also found that about 3% of that same US population were millionaires, most of whom have written goals. We are not trying to make everyone millionaires. However, success ties directly into planning for it. This does not mean that because you plan for success you will automatically have it, but it is pretty certain that if you do not plan for it, you will not.

When you are setting your goals, it is best to use F.A.I.T.H. created by Pastor Rick Warren as mentioned in Chapter five. This acronym will help you set the correct faith steps and enable you to focus on success versus being vague and frustrated:

F - FOCUSED (SPECIFIC) – YOUR GOAL MUST BE CLEAR, NOT VAGUE

A - Attainable (achievable) – You must believe it in faith or don't set it

I - Individual (for you) – Only set a goal for you, not someone else

T - Trackable (measurable) – Be able to track and prove you did it

H - Heartfelt (passionate) – You must be passionate or it won't happen

HOW HAVE YOU SET GOALS IN THE PAST?

WERE THEY LED BY GOD?

· · ·

WERE THEY ACHIEVED?

When you make it a habit of approaching your goals this way, you will find you are very motivated to achieve them and move forward because they are clear and will help you stay focused on your vision. Think smart and act accordingly. Also, study those who do this and follow suit.

Based on this new FAITH acronym, I will now call action steps FAITH steps. Here is an example of a FAITH step that will help you become successful:

"I will begin spending 10 minutes with God every day at 7:00 am by reading a chapter of the Bible and praying, and I will start tomorrow morning."

Here is an example of a Non-FAITH step that will not succeed:

"I will start spending more time with God."

Write two priority goals or habits you believe God would have you work on:

Goal A –

GOAL B –

TIPS FOR FAITH STEP-SETTING:

- Steps of faith do not have to be an action--they could be to pray about or research something
- A step could be one you stick with for a while that turns into a habit (like devotions)
- The right step at the right time will give you peace and excitement, not pressure
- If you don't feel like setting any actions, that is okay; simply think and pray about it

Now, use this chart below and answer yes or no to each question. If you cannot answer "yes" for each question, your FAITH steps need to be adjusted or removed. Use this process for each goal you set and remember to only work on one or two at a time.

GOAL A

GOAL B

IS THE STEP FOCUSED (SPECIFIC)?

IS THE STEP ATTAINABLE?

IS THE STEP INDIVIDUALIZED (FOR YOU)?

IS THE STEP TRACKABLE?

IS IT HEARTFELT?

WERE ALL ANSWERS "YES"?

Time permitting, share one of your FAITH steps with your small group.

Review these steps daily and manage your time to accomplish them. A valuable lesson I have learned and still use to this day is to track my time. Once you begin tracking your time, you will be surprised to find out why you are not accomplishing the things you would like to in life. If you even try tracking your time for one day, you will begin to change your habits of how you pursue your FAITH steps and use your time.

You may also be wondering about all the other goals you listed out and are not yet working on at this time. Keep that list handy and as you move forward and accomplish a step of faith, look again at your list, pray to God about what is next, and plan out the same process. Remember, God will not overwhelm you but will have you work on one or two things at a time.

The other key factor in being successful is accountability. How many goals have you set and let slip by without ever achieving them? Who knew about it? My guess is that you didn't have a success partner (coach, mentor, accountability partner, etc.) at the time. It is easy to let yourself miss a commitment, then another commitment, then finally forget about the whole thing when no one else is looking. Accountability is key! To get help with this, go to www. madetochangetheworld.com. Additionally, if you would like to become a Change the World Coach you can also go to that website for more information.

Make sure to share your FAITH steps with a faithful accountability partner.

One last point: Once you set your steps, ask yourself on a score of 1-10 how confident you are that you can achieve it. If you cannot give it at least an 8, you need to go back to the drawing board and adjust it so that you are very confident you can get it done. It is better to set a very easy goal to achieve success and build momentum than to set a hard goal and miss it. Achieving a FAITH step, no matter how small it is, builds confidence. Missing a step because it is unrealistic at that time will tear down your confidence. One of the best habits you can build is keeping your commitments to God, yourself, and others. Be wise and pray as you set these new steps of faith. God is with you.

V] What did I learn and how will I use it? Takeaways:

- My prayer is...

- What, if anything, do you need to continue working on from last week?

- This week's focus is on surrendering the areas of your life that are not currently surrendered to God so He can lead and bless you in those areas. Pray, then pick the most important area God is calling you to work on first.

- My FAITH step(s):

- What exactly will you do based on God's prompting?

- How will you do it?

- When will you do it?

- What do you need to adjust in order to make this change?

- Who or what can help you get it done (accountability)?

- How confident are you in getting this done?

Is the goal a FAITH goal? Yes or No (if no, make sure to adjust accordingly)

F - FOCUSED (SPECIFIC) – YOUR GOAL MUST BE CLEAR, NOT VAGUE

A - Attainable (achievable) – You must believe it in faith or don't set it

I - Individual (for you) – Only set a goal for you, not someone else

T - Trackable (measurable) – Be able to track and prove you did it

H - Heartfelt (passionate) – You must be passionate or it won't happen

IMPORTANT – Only set a FAITH step you feel very confident you can achieve this next week. There will be a check-in on it next session.

IMPORTANT – Don't forget to record this step in the Action Tracker.

READ THIS CLOSING PRAYER TOGETHER

Lord Jesus, life can be so hard, as you already said it would be. But you also promised that you would never leave me nor forsake me and that I can do all things through you who strengthen me. Help me to live all areas of my life to honor you. Thank you for your plan for me. I believe you have plans to prosper me and not harm me. Plans to give me hope and a future. I seek you with all my heart. Show me the things you have for me and want me to change, pursue, or create. I love you and trust you, Lord. Lead me to love others and do your will. In Jesus' name, Amen.

NEXT STEPS:

- Complete your FAITH step listed above
- Read chapter 9 in *Made to Change the World* for next week
- Have an accountability partner to talk/pray with before next session

SESSION 6

PERSEVERANCE

S ession Focus - from Chapter 9 of the MTCTW book

- Learn how God expects you to persevere.
- Learn how God uses trials to make you stronger and to lead you to maturity in Christ.

Catching Up:

Last week's session was all about taking action in the areas God desires, while having self-control in other important areas of life. How did it go? An important point to remember is that taking action doesn't always mean accomplishing some new activity. I can be praying about something, looking for scriptures, or consulting a mentor. Any movement forward in an area God wants you to work on is a step of faith. Doing what God asks you to do pleases Him.

This session discusses the topic of perseverance. In this day and age many people desire life to go smoothly and without a struggle. The problem is that this fallen world does not work like that. The way we grow strong in the Lord is to go through the struggles together rather than try to avoid all of them.

I] Prayer Requests/ Praise Reports and Prayer

Turn to the back of this book for the section to review previous prayer requests, update answers to prayers, and add additional requests that are mentioned.

Main Scripture

James 1:2-4 says, "Consider it pure joy, my brothers and sisters, whenever you face trials of many kinds because you know that the testing of your faith produces perseverance. Let perseverance finish its work so that you may be mature and complete, not lacking anything."

Surrender Wheel

Take a minute to fill out the Surrender Wheel based on how things went for you this week and how surrendered you were to God in each area.

TAKE THE ASSESSMENT BY RANKING 1-10 BASED ON ASKING GOD HOW WELL you surrender.

1) **Spiritual:**

2) **Mental:**

3) **Physical:**

4) **Family:**

5) **Relationships:**

6) **Career:**

7) **Finances:**

8) **Recreation:**

TOTAL SCORE:

TAKE A LOOK AT YOUR TOTAL SCORE:

HOW ARE YOU DOING WITH THE OUTER CIRCLE OF THE RIM?

1) **Attitude:**

2) **Time:**

3) **Talents:**

TOTAL SCORE

ACCOUNTABILITY

Group members should look at their Surrender Wheel and Spiritual Growth Log at their FAITH step from Session 5. Go around and give a one-minute update to the group on how you did with your goal as well as anything you are still working on from previous sessions.

If you completed your step, congratulations! Record it in your Action Tracker.

If the FAITH step was missed, what is the new plan to be able to reach it this week (be specific)?

A key point to consider is that if you get behind with your steps, complete the original ones first. It is good to only work on 1-2 goals at a time. More than that will easily get you stuck.

•   •   •

II] Overview of the topic & video

In this session, you will learn that as you follow God, life can get hard. Perseverance is key. With the right mindset, a commitment to His will, and putting the right habits in place, you will not only get through the struggle, but you will become stronger in faith and more like Jesus. Your life will impact others and you will change the world.

Small group videos and session notes can be found at madetochangetheworld.com/videos. The password is (all lower case): **mtctwvideos**

Watch Session 6 video

- How do you get through life's challenges?
- Pushing on the Rock: When God Just Doesn't Make Sense
- Do the last thing God has shown you to do.

III] Powerful Questions to Discuss as a Group

- What are the personal life challenges you are facing right now?
- Where do you feel like you are just "pushing a rock" and it's starting to get old?
- What do you feel God is saying to you?
- What promise of God can you "stand on" today?

IV] Going Deeper

Life challenge assessment:

Here is a short assessment to see how faithful you are during life's challenges. In this book or on a piece of paper, rank from 1-5 regarding how strongly each applies to you (1 for never/5 for always):

I always turn to God when things get rough in life.

I believe God will work all my struggles together for good.

I can change.

I can learn new things.

I take full responsibility for my own decisions and attitude.

God is in control.

It is my responsibility to learn and become more like Jesus.

I look at situations with faith rather than fear.

There is a purpose for struggle in this life.

All struggles in life have spiritual implications.

Total

If you scored 46 – 50 then you face problems with the right focus.

If you scored 40 – 44 then you generally have the right focus with some areas to grow.

If you scored 30 - 39 then you have growth areas for facing life's problems.

If you scored less than 30 then you really struggle with life's challenges.

Have a couple people in the group discuss what it was like taking this assessment.

HAVE SOMEONE IN THE GROUP READ OUT LOUD (OR TAKE TURNS reading) the following:

Persevering is the realization that you have not "arrived" on this earth. No matter what you know and who you think you know, God has more to show you. The only way you will fully mature spiritually is to commit fully to God. This means spending time with God and listening to Him. It means to follow Christ as best you can through both good and bad times. It does not mean that when the going gets tough you try to do it all on your own. It does not mean you avoid tough situations. It means that you are willing to go through the struggle while focusing on God and learning in the process.

You may find this commitment to be the toughest thing you will ever do. The choice to continue on and go through it versus turning around and retreating will determine the outcome of the situation and your personal growth. Ask yourself these two questions during the struggle:

1. Do I still trust that God is in control?
2. Will I follow Him regardless of what I see with my own eyes?

The definition of perseverance (from Miriam-Webster Dictionary) is *"Continued effort to do or achieve something despite difficulties, failure, or opposition. The action or condition or an instance of persevering."* Did you notice the word "condition"? We should all have the condition, as Christians, that defaults to seeking, hearing, trusting, and following God by faith. This should be our condition no matter what is happening in the world around us.

The word used in American Standard and King James versions of the Bible instead of perseverance is "patience". Perseverance means *"Bearing pains or traits calmly and without complaint; steadfast despite opposition, difficulty, or adversity."* In today's culture, the goal for many people is to have pleasure and avoid pain. In God's plan, there are times of struggle and they will transform you toward godliness if you let them.

There are some situations that you should not be in and God will get you out of right away. There are other situations where God wants you to remain in order to grow in your faith.

How will you know when God wants you to stay vs. moving on?

How will you persevere with God where He wants you to remain?

. . .

V] WHAT DID I LEARN AND HOW WILL I USE IT? TAKEAWAYS:

- My prayer is...

- What, if anything, do you need to continue working on from previous weeks?

- This week's focus is on perseverance. What does God want you to focus on this week? One idea is to seek him in your areas of struggle and ask where He wants you to move on and where He wants you to stay, then come up with plans for each.

- My FAITH step(s):

- What exactly will you do based on God's prompting?

- How will you do it?

- When will you do it?

- What do you need to adjust in order to make this change?

- Who or what can help you get it done (accountability)?

- How confident are you in getting this done?

Is the goal a FAITH step? Yes or No (if no, make sure to adjust accordingly)

F - FOCUSED (SPECIFIC) – YOUR GOAL MUST BE CLEAR, NOT VAGUE

A - Attainable (achievable) – You must believe it in faith or don't set it

I - Individual (for you) – Only set a goal for you, not someone else

T - Trackable (measurable) – Be able to track and prove you did it

H - Heartfelt (passionate) – You must be passionate or it won't happen

IMPORTANT – Only set a step you feel very confident you can achieve this next week. There will be a check-in on it next session.

IMPORTANT – Don't forget to record this FAITH step in the Action Tracker.

READ THIS CLOSING PRAYER TOGETHER

Dear Jesus, you are my all. I trust in you, even when times are tough. I know that you said there will be challenges in this world but not to worry because you have overcome this world. Help me to remain true to you every day. Please strengthen me, guide me, and direct me. I love you. Please bring your peace that passes all understanding into my heart and soul. I will be who you made me to be. Help me also to love and support those who struggle around me. In Jesus' name, Amen.

Next Steps:

- Complete your FAITH step listed above
- Read chapter 10 in *Made to Change the World* for next week
- Have an accountability partner to talk/pray with before next session

SESSION 7
ENERGY

S ession Focus - from Chapter 10 of the MTCTW book

- How God designed you and this world
- How to have the energy to carry out God's plan

CATCHING UP:

Last week, the focus was on persevering through life's struggles by walking with God. Perseverance is not easy, but is very effective in helping us become like Jesus if our focus is on Him. How did this area go for you this past week? Important reminders: 1) Ask God if the thing you are persevering through is His plan, 2) If it is His plan, focus on Him as He leads you to persevere and overcome.

This session will be covering the powerful topic of where our energy comes from and how to maintain it to carry out God's plan. Don't confuse the word "energy" with the world's definition. God is the source of all life and energy in this world, including yours.

. . .

I] PRAYER REQUESTS/ PRAISE REPORTS AND PRAYER

Turn to the back of this book for the section to review previous prayer requests, update answers to prayers, and add additional requests that are mentioned.

Main Scripture

1 Peter 1:16 says, "Be holy because I am holy."

Surrender Wheel

Take a minute to fill out the Surrender Wheel based on how things went for you this week and how surrendered you were to God in each area.

TAKE THE ASSESSMENT BY RANKING 1-10 HOW BASED ON ASKING GOD HOW well you surrender.

1) Spiritual:

2) Mental:

3) Physical:

4) Family:

5) Relationships:

6) **Career:**

7) **Finances:**

8) **Recreation:**

TOTAL SCORE

Take a look at your total score:

How are you doing with the outer circle of the rim?

1) **Attitude:**

2) **Time:**

3) **Talents:**

TOTAL SCORE:

Accountability:

Group members should look at their Surrender Wheel and Spiritual Growth Log at their goal from Session 6. Go around and give a one-minute update to the group on how you did with your FAITH step as well as anything you are still working on from previous sessions.

If you completed your step, congratulations! Record it in your Action Tracker.

If the step was missed, what is the new plan to be able to reach it this week (be specific)?

A key point to consider is that if you get behind with your FAITH steps, complete the original ones first, keeping in mind that it is best to work on 1-2 goals at a time. More than that will easily get you stuck.

II] Overview of the topic & video

In this session, you will discuss what it means to fully live your purpose. This means having the energy and momentum for the long-term commitment to live for God. You will also be able to determine action steps to continually help you move forward.

Small group videos and session notes can be found at madetochangetheworld.com/videos. The password is (all lower case): **mtctwvideos**

WATCH SESSION 7 VIDEO

- Having it all: Kate Spade
- What does "moving forward" mean?
- Mexican Fisherman story

III] POWERFUL QUESTIONS TO DISCUSS AS A GROUP: (10 MINUTES)

- What is it in life that you want?
- When you play that desire out, where does it lead?
- Is it God putting this desire in your heart, or does it come from somewhere else?
- How are you continuing to grow?
- As you grow in your faith and relationship with God, what commitment will you make today to surrender, become accountable, and know exactly what you are called to do?

IV] GOING DEEPER

Have someone in the group read out loud (or take turns reading) the following:

1. **Continually Surrender.** Walking with God is not about how much you can do for Him and prove to others. It is about what you will turn over to Him and follow. Every day you should be surrendering all that you have and all that you are to Him. When you hold onto things, you begin taking over for God, but when you turn them over, you are letting God be God in your life. What I like to do periodically in my devotional time is lay face down and in my mind think of all the things God has given me and has done for me then turn them all back over to Him to use as He wants.

ONE POWERFUL EXAMPLE OF THIS THAT HIT HOME IN MY LIFE MANY YEARS ago was when Claudia and I were getting ready to move back to California. We had literally everything we owned in a moving truck parked in my parents' drive that night and as I was getting ready for bed I realized that if someone stole the truck, everything we owned would be gone. Everything. And I was okay with that. The most important things in my life are not things; they are people. My Heavenly Father, my wife, my family, and those around me whom God has called me to love are what truly matters.

How will you commit to surrender your life to God today?

2. **HAVE ACCOUNTABILITY.** WHEN YOU LIVE AS AN ISLAND UNTO YOURSELF and resist letting anyone in, you are bound to stumble and not have any help to get up. Instead, be accountable to God. Allow Him into every area of your life so that He may show you, lead you and guide you. When you fall or when you fail, come to Him. He already knows the situation, but when you humble yourself in accountability, He will lift you up to rise above. I think of raising Ellie, who came onto this earth without knowing anything and needing to learn everything as she grows. As I help her learn and grow, step by step, I grow closer to her and it brings me joy. That is how your Heavenly Father wants to be with you.

Also, be accountable to others. My wife and I are very close. I am accountable to her on all levels and she to me. We grow together in this way. I am also accountable to my brother-in-law, Jonathan. Every week we pray together, talk about our balance with each other, confess our shortfalls, and support each other. I also have accountability through coaching for following the Purpose, Mission, and Vision God has for me to help me stay on His track. Who are the people in your life who keep you accountable?

Who can you be accountable to? How and when will you do this?

3. Know that you know. I will never forget the words spoken directly to me by my mentor, Zig Ziglar. After spending 45 minutes with him one day backstage at a large event in Cleveland, Ohio, Zig looked me in the eye and said, "Brian, I know that I know that I know that I am doing exactly what God has called me to do and I will continue to do so until I leave this earth." It gave me chills! How can you absolutely know you are doing what God has called you to do? That is what I wanted and what I believe I am doing today.

You can absolutely know God and know that you are being and doing what He wants you to be and do. In the Bible, God says, "You will seek me and find me when you seek me with all your heart" Jeremiah 29:13 (NIV). If your focus is to seek God, not only will you find Him, but He will lead you day by day and step by step. As I mentioned before, my purpose for each day is to believe as I go to lay my head on my pillow that God says to me, "Well done, good and faithful servant" Matthew 25:23 (NIV). If you strive to know God, hear God, and follow Him, everything else in your life will come together through Him and you will be a world-changer.

What do you need God to show you to know so you can know you are in His plan each day?

Keeping up your energy to follow God

Although some of the following may sound like worldly knowledge, I believe there are things in science that prove how God has made us and validates what gives us energy in this life to do the things we're designed to do. Science simply tries to explain what God has created.

Keeping up your energy requires that you do the things that increase it and avoid the things that decrease it. Here is a list of areas to rank for yourself:

Answer how you typically do in these areas that impact "electrical" energy:

1. Spend a relaxed time with God (meditating on Him, prayer, scripture) daily
2. Get enough sleep each night for your body and mind to recover
3. Exercise and move your body (as we were designed to do from Genesis)
4. Learn something new to stretch your mind
5. Read motivating and uplifting material
6. Focus on the Purpose, Mission, and Vision God has given you
7. Have God-directed goals you are working towards
8. Focus on God and don't give in to fear
9. Correct any mental "addictions" such as pornography, lying, cheating, etc.
10. Give gratitude to God and others

Answer how you typically do in these areas that impact your "chemical balance":

1. Put healthy foods into your body
2. Eat the right amount of food for your body
3. Generally avoid unhealthy foods (sugar, alcohol, chemically-altered, etc.)
4. Avoid drug-related chemicals (except as prescribed by doctors)
5. Correct any chemical addictions to food, smoking, alcohol, drugs, etc.

What, if anything, do you need to change to increase your energy (only start with one thing):

V] What did I learn and how will I use it? Takeaways:

- My prayer is...

- What, if anything, do you need to continue working on from previous weeks?

- This week's focus is on keeping up your energy. What do you feel God wants you to focus on this week?

- My FAITH step(s):

- What exactly will you do based on God's prompting?

- How will you do it?

- When will you do it?

- What do you need to adjust in order to make this change?

- Who or what can help you get it done (accountability)?

- How confident are you in getting this done?

Is the goal a FAITH step? Yes or No (if no, make sure to adjust accordingly)

F - Focused (specific) – Your goal must be clear, not vague

A - Attainable (achievable) – You must believe it in faith or don't set it

I - Individual (for you) – Only set a goal for you, not someone else

T - Trackable (measurable) – Be able to track and prove you did it

H - Heartfelt (passionate) – You must be passionate or it won't happen

IMPORTANT – Only set a FAITH step you feel very confident you can achieve this next week. There will be a check-in on it next session.

IMPORTANT – Don't forget to record this step in the Action Tracker.

Read this closing prayer together:

Dear Lord Jesus, you are my everything. I want to be holy as you are holy. Please cleanse me and lead me every day. Help me know that I know that I know your voice and that I am being and doing exactly what you want me to be and do each day until the day I go to be with you. I live to love you and others. Help me to live life in such a way as to hear "well done good and faithful servant" at the end of each day. In Jesus' name, Amen.

. . .

NEXT STEPS:

- Complete your FAITH step listed above
- Read the Epilogue in *Made to Change the World* for next week
- Have an accountability partner to talk/pray with before next session

SESSION 8

CELEBRATION

Session Focus - from Chapter 10 and Epilogue of MTCTW book

- To live a faithful, impactful, and adventurous life for Christ
- To celebrate what God has done in your life and group

CATCHING UP:

Last week's session was about how God made this world and the energy He gives us to do His will. God is the creating and sustaining force of this universe and everything in it. God gives us all the time and energy we need in this world to be able to do what He calls us to do. However, it is our responsibility to live in a way that enables our bodies and minds to have all the energy they need.

This session will cover how to live the life of world impact that God is calling you to and celebrate the fact that He is with you, leading and guiding you every step of the way. God has already done amazing things in your life and group, and it's time to thank Him for it.

RECOMMENDED: Stay after the normal group time to talk, laugh, and catch up. Consider also eating together or planning a time to go out to eat or do something social. Bless others as you do.

I] PRAYER REQUESTS/ PRAISE REPORTS AND PRAYER

Turn to the back of this book for the section to review previous prayer requests, update answers to prayers, and add additional requests that are mentioned.

MAIN SCRIPTURE

JAMES 1:22 SAYS, "DO NOT MERELY LISTEN TO THE WORD, AND SO DECEIVE yourselves. Do what it says."

SURRENDER WHEEL

Take a minute to fill out the Surrender Wheel based on how things went for you this week and how surrendered you were to God in each area.

CHRISTIAN SURRENDER WHEEL

TAKE THE ASSESSMENT BY RANKING 1-10 BASED ON ASKING GOD HOW WELL you surrender.

1) Spiritual:

2) Mental:

3) Physical:

4) Family:

5) Relationships:

6) **Career:**

7) **Finances:**

8) **Recreation:**

TOTAL SCORE:

TAKE A LOOK AT YOUR TOTAL SCORE:

How are you doing with the outer circle of the rim:

1) **Attitude:**

2) **Time:**

3) **Talents:**

TOTAL SCORE:

ACCOUNTABILITY

Group members should look at their Surrender Wheel and Spiritual Growth Log at their goal from Session 6. Go around and give a one-minute update to the group on how you did with your FAITH step as well as anything you are still working on from previous sessions.

If you completed your step of faith, congratulations! Record it in your Action Tracker.

If the FAITH step was missed, what is the new plan to be able to reach it this week (be specific)?

A key point to consider is that if you get behind with your FAITH steps, complete the original ones first. It is good to work on 1-2 goals at a time. More than that will easily get you stuck.

II] OVERVIEW OF THE TOPIC & VIDEO

In this session, you will discuss the ways in which God may be calling you to do new things to Change the World. You may not realize it, but everything you do, no matter how little or insignificant it seems, has an impact. There may be other little things you could do or change that will impact those around you with the love of God.

Small group videos and session notes can be found at madetochangetheworld.com/videos. The password is (all lower case): **mtctwvideos**

Watch Session 8 video

- Michelangelo's *David*
- The one most important thing – spend time with your Father and Savior
- Parable of the talents

III] Powerful Questions to Discuss as a Group

- What does God need to still chip away in you?
- How much time are you spending each day with your Father and Savior?
- What is God showing you when you meet with him?
- What are you doing with your talents?

IV] Going Deeper

New ideas to help change the world (read independently then discuss as a group)

. . .

HERE ARE SOME IDEAS GOD MAY USE TO SPUR YOU INTO ACTION TO CHANGE the world. As you do anything with your time, talent, and treasures, be someone who is willing to share the love of Jesus through prayer, encouragement, and your personal witness.

Time:

- Volunteer at church
- Volunteer to feed the hungry
- Volunteer to help orphans
- Visit people who are lonely
- Visit the elderly
- Invite someone to pray with you
- Start a small group
- Become a foster parent
- Adopt a child
- Sign up for a prayer ministry
- Coordinate a block party, then pray before dinner
- Invite neighbors to church
- Go on a mission trip
- Call the person who offended you and make peace
- Spend an hour per day with your children
- Eat with your family and ask what God has done in their lives
- Do something unexpected for a neighbor
- Ask your closest friend if they have ever accepted Jesus
- Ask your family members if they have ever accepted Jesus
- Tell those around you that you love and care for them

Talent:

- Make a meal for someone
- Draw a picture for someone
- Sing
- Create something new
- Write a book
- Lead a church group
- Teach kids or adults about Jesus

- Plan a day trip to be with your family
- Help someone with their finances
- Smile and make conversation with others
- Get into ministry
- Encourage someone who is down
- Help others find and use their talents
- Become a Coach
- Play on a sports team
- Help someone organize his/her house

Treasures:

- Tithe 10% of your income to church
- Give to ministries
- Give to others around you in need
- Give away unused clothes
- Give away unused toys
- Buy Christian books for others (I can think of a really good one)
- Share your home
- Give to the poor
- Feed the homeless
- Donate a car to a family in need
- Give airline tickets or miles to someone in need
- Give away winter wear to those who are cold
- Pay someone's toll road ticket
- Pay someone's utility bill
- Ask your Pastor what is needed for the church
- Support someone going on a mission trip

Do any of these ideas spur you on to do something new or different?

PUTTING IT ALL TOGETHER (READ TOGETHER THEN ANSWER YES/NO ON **your own)**

Let us put all of this together. You have just read a book about how you are Made To Change The World. Maybe you laughed at some stories and cried at others. Hopefully, you learned some new things and felt inspired along the way. Most likely, you found something you can take away from this book.

I want to challenge you now to realize that it doesn't really matter if you liked or didn't like the book or whether or not you learned something new. What really matters most is how you will act upon what you read. Learning is one thing and doing is quite another. Similarly, you can say you have faith, or you can actually live out your faith.

Let's look at the chapters of this book and I want you to put a "yes" or "no" based on each chapter to answer if you are actually doing it or not. The chapters are listed as building blocks so wherever you write your first "no" is the place for you to start. That may mean you will need to re-read that chapter. Think about it and pray about it.

Determine how and when you will take action upon it.

Chapter 1 – Do you have a perspective of life like Jerome that your life matters?

Chapter 2 – Have you written out your life purpose and committed to living it?

Chapter 3 – Are you putting only truth in your mind and turning away from all else?

Chapter 4 – Are you sure of what you hope for and certain of what you do not see?

Chapter 5 – Are you acting upon your faith and not just saying you have faith?

Chapter 6 – Do you have self-control in the areas where God asks you to?

Chapter 7 – Is your life in balance with Jesus as the central hub?

Chapter 8 – Are you persevering and learning what God wants you to right now?

Chapter 9 – Do you have a plan and are you letting God direct your steps?

Chapter 10 – Are you fully living your purpose today?

V] WHAT DID I LEARN AND HOW WILL I USE IT? TAKEAWAYS:

- Share with each other what you are thankful for about God and each other.
- My prayer is...
- What, if anything, do you need to continue working on?
- This week's focus is on celebrating God daily and considering how else to change the world around you. What do you feel God wants you to focus on this week?
- My FAITH step(s):
- What exactly will you do based on God's prompting?
- How will you do it?
- When will you do it?
- What do you need to adjust in order to make this change?
- Who or what can help you get it done (accountability)?
- How confident are you in getting this done?

Is the goal a FAITH step? Yes or No (if no, make sure to adjust accordingly)

F - Focused (specific) – Your goal must be clear, not vague

A - Attainable (achievable) – You must believe it in faith or don't set it

I - Individual (for you) – Only set a goal for you, not someone else

T - Trackable (measurable) – Be able to track and prove you did it

H - Heartfelt (passionate) – You must be passionate or it won't happen

IMPORTANT – Only set a step of faith you feel very confident you can achieve this next week. There will be a check-in on it next session.

IMPORTANT – Don't forget to record this faith step in the Action Tracker.

Read this closing prayer together:

Dear Lord Jesus, lead me. Guide me. Show me your way. I celebrate you as my Father, Lord, and Savior. My time on this earth is limited, so help me use my time, talents, and resources for you in every way and every day. Bless my brothers and sisters in Christ. Keep them and lead them also to do your will.

Next Steps:

- Determine if you will continue to meet as a group (highly encouraged)
- Every week, continue to complete the Weekly Check-ins at the back of this book
- Have an accountability partner to talk/pray with to help you stay on track

For additional studies based off Made to Change the World, here are some options:

Session 1 – Perspective – Use book *Walk with God Today*

Session 2 – Purpose – Use book *Directions for Life*

Session 3 – Truth and Faith – Use book *Talk Truth to Yourself*

Session 4 – Change and Balance – Use book *Life Balance for Christians*

Session 5 – Action and Self-Control – Use book *Theology of Behavior Change*

Session 6 – Perseverance – Use book *Lifewise: How to Live by God's Wisdom*

Session 7 – Energy – Use book *The Daniel Plan* by Rick Warren

Session 8 – Celebration – Use your group prayer list to continually pray and give thanks

You can find most of these additional resources as well as where to connect with a Christian Life Coach if you would like to do so at www. madetochangetheworl.com/resources.

CHRISTIAN SURRENDER WHEEL

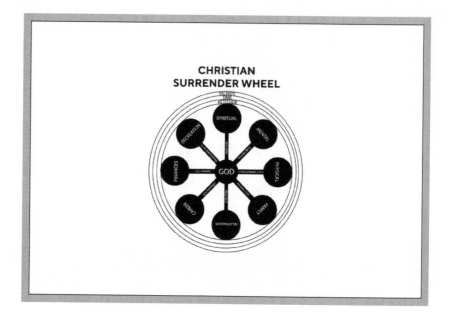

Take the assessment by ranking 1-10 based on asking God how well you surrender.

1) Spiritual:

2) Mental:

3) Physical:

4) Family:

5) Relationships:

6) Career:

7) Finances:

8) Recreation:

TOTAL SCORE:

Take a look at your total score:

If you scored over 65: You have a good overall balance in surrendering to God.

If you scored under 65: You can probably feel your life is out of balance for God.

What area is the highest? You can probably think of reasons why it is so high.

What area is the lowest? You can probably also think of reasons why it is so low.

How are you doing with the outer circle of the rim:

1) Attitude:

2) Time:

3) Talents:

TOTAL SCORE:

Under 25: You probably have some things you would like to improve, especially since these areas directly relate to you fulfilling your purpose in life. Ask yourself the same questions as those above for the eight areas of the balance wheel.

If you would like to know more and grow deeper in the areas where you are needing to change, consider purchasing the surrender wheel book (called *The Surrender Wheel - Christian Life Balance is Not What You Think)* to see the specific areas of the spoke you are working on to help you to identify what and where to change to glorify God. You can find the surrender wheel book at www.madetochangetheworld.com or on Amazon.

FAITH GOALS TOOL

F - Focused (specific) – Your goal must be clear, not vague

A - Attainable (achievable) – You must believe it in faith or don't set it

I - Individual (for you) – Only set a goal for you, not someone else

T - Trackable (measurable) – Be able to track and prove you did it

H - Heartfelt (passionate) – You must be passionate or it won't happen

My goal is to…

Is this goal Focused (specific)?

Is the goal Attainable?

Is the goal Individualized (for you)?

Is the goal Trackable?

Is it Heartfelt?

Were all answers "yes"?

SMALL GROUP PRAYER LIST

Name/Request:

Name/Request:

Name/Request:

Name/Request:

Name/Request:

Name/Request:

Name/Request:

Name/Request:

Name/Request:

Name/Request:

HOW TO USE THE WEEKLY
CHECK-IN

The eight-session study of *Made to Change the World* is ending, but that does not end your walk with God or your growth of faith. There is an exciting adventure to continue. The first recommendation is to continue meeting as a group and growing together. One of the most important things you can do is keep communication and accountability as part of your life because the enemy would love to isolate you.

There are many great studies available by many different Christian authors. If you would like to continue going deeper with how you started growing with *Made to Change the World,* see additional studies listed below.

Now what?

1. Keep meeting as a group
2. Pick the study you would like to go through next
3. Whatever study you use next, always start your groups with the following check-ins
4. It should only take 5-10 minutes but will continue what you have started here

IMPORTANT NOTE: Behavior change generally occurs after you have done something routinely for six months or more. That becomes your new norm and is why there is an additional four months of check ins.

Stay on track, stay accountable, stay in Christ. You will be amazed at how He uses you!

Additional Study Ideas by Brian Williams:

- Directions For Life – knowing and living your life purpose, mission, and vision
- Talk Truth to Yourself – Live by God's truth and not the lies of the evil one
- Life Balance for Christians: It's Not What You Think– Dig deeper into the areas of the wheel you want to grow in
- Theology of Behavior Change – Learn more about how human behavior change works. Go to madetochangetheworld.com for this book.
- Walk With God Today – Devotional to help you walk more closely with God

WEEKLY CHECK-IN BALANCE WHEEL

Weekly Check-in on Balance & Goals: Week __

Take the assessments by ranking 1-10 based on asking God how well you surrender.

1) Spiritual:

2) Mental:

3) Physical:

4) Family:

5) Relationships:

6) **Career:**

7) **Finances:**

8) **Recreation:**

TOTAL SCORE:

My FAITH Goal(s) Follow-Up

What was **Goal A** from last week?

Did I achieve it? Why or why not?

If achieved, who can you share the success with?

If not achieved, what do you need to adjust this week?

Is this a goal you feel God would have you continue?

What was **Goal B** from last week?

Did I achieve it? Why or why not?

If achieved, who can you share the success with?

If not achieved, what do you need to adjust this week?

Is this a goal you feel God would have you continue?

Additional areas:

1) **Attitude:**

2) **Time:**

3) **Talents:**

TOTAL SCORE:

My specific FAITH goal(s) for this week:

Made in the USA
Columbia, SC
24 July 2021